Catch

A

Little

Rhyme

Catch

A

Pictures by Imero Gobbato

Little

Rhyme

Eve Merriam

ATHENEUM, NEW YORK 1966

FOR BRADLEY MICHAEL

CONTENTS

Catch
A
Little
Rhyme

Once upon a time
I caught a little rhyme

I set it on the floor
but it ran right out the door

I chased it on my bicycle
but it melted to an icicle

I scooped it up in my hat
but it turned into a cat

I caught it by the tail
but it stretched into a whale

I followed it in a boat
but it changed into a goat

When I fed it tin and paper
it became a tall skyscraper

Then it grew into a kite
and flew far out of sight . . .

INSIDE THE ZOO

If you were an animal inside the zoo,
And creatures called people came looking at you,
How would you like it and what would you do?

Well, if you were a bear, you'd have to guffaw:
How funny people look with two legs and not four.

And if you were a zebra, you surely would grin:
How funny people look without stripes on their skin.

Or if you were a giraffe, you'd laugh, I expect:
How funny people look with no stretchable neck.

And if you were an elephant, you'd galumph, I suppose:
How funny people look with no hose for a nose.

But if you were a monkey, you'd cheer through and through:
How *handsome* people look—looking so much like you!

SCHENECTADY

Although I've been to Kankakee
And Kalamazoo and Kokomo,
The place I've always wanted to go,
The city I've always wanted to see
Is Schenectady.

Schenectady, Schenectady,
Though it's hard to pronounce correctly,
I plan to go there directly.

Schenectady, Schenectady,
Yes, I want to connect with Schenectady,
The town I select is Schenectady,
I elect to go to Schenectady,
I'll take any trek to Schenectady,
Even wash my neck for Schenectady,
So expect me next at Schenectady,
Check and double check
Schenectady!

OLLIE'S POLLY

Ollie
has a polly-bird.
The only word
that bird can say
all the livelong
night and day
is

Quiet!
    Quiet!!
        Quiet!!!

When neighbors call to stop that riot,
Ollie's polly shouts back
QUIET!

ANN'S FAN

Ann
has a watering can
and a frying pan
and a Japanese fan
with a picture on it of Ann
    with a watering can
    and a frying pan
    and a Japanese fan

with a picture on it of Ann
   with a watering can
   and a frying pan
   and a Japanese fan . . .

FRED'S BED

Fred
uses his bed
for a sled,
and the floor below
for snow.

When his head bumps the floor,
it's not so nice:
the soft snow has turned
hard into ice.
Oh!

PETE'S SWEETS

Pete
will eat
anything
if it's sweet.

Peppermint soup,
or ice cream on toast.

Though what he likes most
is a jelly sandwich
without any bread.

Or instead,
a bubble-gum chop.
Chew your meat thoroughly, Pete.
   "I am. Cancha hear me?" Pop!

BAM, BAM, BAM

Pickaxes, pickaxes swinging today,
Plaster clouds flying every which way.

Workmen are covered with white dust like snow,
Oh, come see the great demolition show!

Slam, slam, slam,
Goes the steel wrecking-ball;
Bam, bam, bam,
Against a stone wall.

It's raining bricks and wood
In my neighborhood.
Down go the houses,
Down go the stores,
Up goes a building
With forty-seven floors.

Crash goes a chimney,
Pow goes a hall,
Zowie goes a doorway,
Zam goes a wall.

Slam, slam, slam,
Goes the steel wrecking-ball;
Bam, bam, bam,
Changing it all.

DICK'S TRICK

Dick
can pick up his heels
and make them click.

Sometimes, in the damp air,
they stick there . . .

JUNE'S TUNE

June
has a tune
in her head.

When it's time for bed,
she'll go just as soon
as you sing her the tune

that nobody knows
except
June.

GOING TO SCHOOL

Going to school
I pass a street
where there is a hardware store
and next to it
a flower shop.

I like to stop
and greet
the flowers on display,
then see next door
different kinds of blooms:
bright paint cans,
shiny pots and pans,
a bouquet
of mops and brooms.

BIG GOLIATH, LITTLE DAVID

The shepherd boy was David,
Just a little lad;
Goliath was the giant,
Big, so big and bad.

"Bow down to me!" Goliath roared,
"For I am big and you are small!
Bow down to me, little David—
To the mighty giant tall!"

"I won't," said David, "I'm not scared
Of you just because you're taller;
I can be brave as anyone—
No matter if I am smaller.

"And you're not tall as a pine tree
That towers to the sky,
While I can climb that pine tree
Up to its branches high."

Goliath stamped his giant foot
And frowned his giant's frown:
"*Bow down to me* is what I said!
Bow down! Bow down! Bow down!"

But little David, quick as quick,
Climbed high into the tall pine tree;
He fastened a slingshot with a stone
Before Goliath could see—

Then little David took careful aim
And zing he let his slingshot go:
The mighty giant was no more,
Little David had laid him low!

"Oh, I'm not afraid of a giant
Or anything that's big and tall—boo!
It's more fun to be small and grow
With the whole world stretched before you!"

"BOW DOWN! BOW DOWN!"

"I won't . . .

I won't . . ."

KING SOLOMON

King Solomon was such a wise old king
That people came to ask him everything.
They asked questions that would baffle you or me,
But Solomon could answer them—one, two, three!

"Solomon, King Solomon, you're such a wise man,
Try to answer this question if you can!

"What's the happiest music to be heard?
Is it the song of the nightingale bird?
The quivering note of a violin string?
A silver bell with a golden ring?
A piano playing a thunderous note?
An accordion that folds like a paper boat?
A merry-go-round at a county fair?
A circus band in the village square?

We will cross deserts and climb mountains, too,
In search of the answer we seek now from you."

King Solomon smiled: "You needn't roam,
For the answer you seek is close to home.

The happiest music to be heard
Is not the song of the nightingale bird,
The quivering tone of a violin string,
A silver bell with a golden ring,
A piano playing a thunderous note,
An accordion that folds like a paper boat,
A merry-go-round at a county fair,
A circus band in the great town square—

"No, the happiest music that there can be
Is a boy or girl whistling in an apple tree!"

"King Solomon, King Solomon, then tell us true
The answer to the second riddle we ask of you:
What is the strongest ship that can sail?
That won't bend or break in the stormiest gale?"

Solomon thought for a moment or two,
Then he said, "The ship for me and for you
That will hold calm and steady to the end of the trip
Is the one that we share best—it is good friend-ship."

"Solomon, King Solomon, you're such a wise man,
Answer this last riddle if you can:
What's sweeter than sugar or jam or honey
And what you can't buy for barrels of money?"

Solomon looked low, Solomon looked high,
First down at the ground, then up at the sky;
The sun was like a daffodil yellow and bright,
And a blade of April grass was dancing in the light.
"Oh, sweeter than sugar or jam or honey,
And what you can't buy—not for barrels of money,
Is the sweetest treasure that nature can bring:
That after winter there always comes spring!"

HAPPY BIRTHDAY TO ME

It's my birthday
And everyone says
I'm growing up.

But look—
My arms are growing down!
See my last year's sleeves?

SOMETIMES

Sometimes I share things,
And everyone says
"Isn't it lovely? Isn't it fine?"

I give my little brother
Half my ice cream cone
And let him play
With toys that are mine.

But today
I don't feel like sharing.
Today
I want to be let alone.
Today
I don't want to give my little brother
A single thing except
A shove.

WEATHER

Dot a dot dot   dot a dot dot
Spotting the windowpane.
Spack a spack speck   flick a flack fleck
Freckling the windowpane.

A spatter a scatter   a wet cat a clatter
A splatter a rumble outside.
Umbrella umbrella umbrella umbrella
Bumbershoot barrel of rain.

Slosh a galosh   slosh a galosh
Slither and slather and glide
A puddle a jump a puddle a jump
A puddle a jump puddle splosh
A juddle a pump aluddle a dump a
Puddmuddle jump in and slide!

ALLIGATOR ON THE ESCALATOR

Through the revolving door
Of a department store
There slithered an alligator.

When he came to the escalator,
He stepped upon the track with great dexterity;
His tail draped over the railing,
And he clicked his teeth in glee:

"Yo, I'm off on the escalator,
Excited as I can be!
It's a *moving* experience,
As you can plainly see.
On the moving stair I go anywhere,
I rise to the top
Past outerwear, innerwear,
Dinnerware, thinnerwear—
Then down to the basement with bargains galore,
Then back on the track to the top once more!
Oh, I may ride the escalator
Until closing time or later,
So tell the telephone operator
To call Mrs. Albert Q. Alligator
And tell her to take a hot mud bath
And not to wait up for me!"

ON OUR WAY

What kind of walk shall we take today?
Leap like a frog? Creep like a snail?
Scamper like a squirrel with a furry tail?

Flutter like a butterfly? Chicken peck?
Stretch like a turtle with a poking-out neck?

Trot like a pony, clip clop clop?
Swing like a monkey in a treetop?

Scuttle like a crab? Kangaroo jump?
Plod like a camel with an up-and-down hump?

We could even try a brand new way—
Walking down the street
On our own two feet.

PECULIAR

I once knew a boy who was odd as could be:
He liked to eat cauliflower and broccoli
And spinach and turnips and rhubarb pies
And he didn't like hamburgers or French fries.

BACKWARDS

If the alphabet ran backwards,
We'd have to learn to say
Our ZYX's
Instead of ABC's

Oh,
First, we'd go
Z-Y-X,
Then W-V would come next.

U-T-S,
Yes, that's so,
R-Q-P
On we go

To O-N-M,
Then L-K-J
In our backward letters way

Until we see
I-H-G,
F-E-D
and last of all we come to say
C-B-A!

There must be
An alphabetter way.
Let's turn our letters back again:
Then see what we
Can A-B-C!

"Me oh my," said the tiny, shiny ant,
"I can crawl all the way up a sand hill.
A hill so high it's as big as a thimble.
Can any creature in the world be bigger than I?"

"Skat," said the green caterpillar,
"I can inch myself all the way across a twig.
Now a twig is really *big!*
Hooray for great, glorious, mammoth, and modest me."

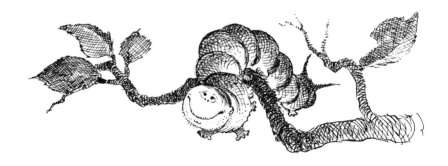

"Gog and magog," said the speckled frog,
"And bilge water. Little ant, crawly caterpillar,
You can only creep.
I can leap!
All the way up to a tremendous lily pad in the pond.
How superiffic can any creature be?
I'll tell you—
He can be me!"

"Oh," laughed the little boy,
"Gangway, skedaddle, vamoose.
Look at me, tiny ant. My finger is bigger than a thimble.
Look, inchy caterpillar. My foot is bigger than a twig.
Look, speckled frog. My hand can cover a lily pad all over.
Why, I'm so big I can run in circles, I can run in squares,

I can reach to tables, I can fill up chairs!
And I'm still growing!
When I grow all the way up, my head will bump the sky.
I'll have clouds for a bed, and a moon pillow,
And stars instead of freckles on my nose."

(*Is that how big a little boy grows?*)

TEEVEE

In the house
of Mr. and Mrs. Spouse
he and she
would watch teevee
and never a word
between them spoken
until the day
the set was broken.

Then "How do you do?"
said he to she,
"I don't believe
that we've met yet.
Spouse is my name.
What's yours?" he asked.

"Why, mine's the same!"
said she to he,
"Do you suppose that we could be—?"

But the set came suddenly right about,
and so they never did find out.

DING, DING

Somebody else can be captain,
Somebody else can be king,
I'd rather be the man with a cart
And a little bell to ring.

Ding, ding. Ding, ding.
It's spring again and ice cream time.
Who wants an orange popsicle?
Who wants a lemon or lime?

I dream of being the man with a cart
And a little bell to ring.
I'd tell all my friends to gather round
And they wouldn't need money to bring.

Ding, ding. Ding, ding.
Have a cone or a cup or a float,
And as for myself all I would take
Is a double banana boat.

Ding, ding. Ding, ding. Ding, ding!

THE DONKEY AND THE FLUKE

A donkey caught a fluke swimming round in the sea,
And the fluke said "Donkey, please listen to me;
I'm a magic fish and if you'll let me go free,
I'll grant all your wishes to the number of three."

So the donkey dropped the fluke back in the sea,
And in return for letting that fish go free:
He asked for the first of his magic wishes three:
A clever talking parrot to keep him company.

Now that was the first of the donkey's wishes three:
A clever talking parrot to keep him company.

Well, a parrot soon appeared, but, alas, all it could say
Was what the donkey muttered to himself every day:
"Heehaw, heehaw, heehaw, hee,
Heehaw, heehaw, hee, hee, hee!"

The donkey grew disgusted with that ignorant bird
That didn't have the brains to say a single learned word,
And he wished for a parrot that wouldn't sound absurd—
A parrot that could parrot some more sensible word.

So that was the second of the donkey's wishes three:
A parrot to converse more intelligently.

Soon the donkey was delighted, completely satisfied
With the new bird that flew in to perch by his side,
For *this* parrot was so clever, its beak could open wide
And speak in intellectual accents dignified:
"Hawhee, hawhee, haw, hee, hee,
Hawhee, hawhee, haw, haw, hee!"

Then the donkey spurned the last of the fish's wishes three,
Nothing more he wanted—he was blissful as could be;
So that fluke is still floundering confounded in the sea
With one more wish to give away: perhaps to you or me!

Hawhee, hawhee, haw, hee, hee,
Heehaw, heehaw, hee, haw, hee!

One is a number that may be conceited,
That thinks of itself as sweet honey or jam:
For one is the number of people I am.

Two is the usual number for shoes.
Is it because one's too easy to lose?

Half circle and then a half circle again.
Though *three* feels it's boring to be so repeated,
Still, it is far better off incompleted.
For if its two halves into one whole were caught,
Then all that is three would amount to just naught.

Four makes the legs for a table or chair.
It can do the same thing for a tiger or bear.

Five is a highway going straight and then
It takes a sharp left and turns right round again.

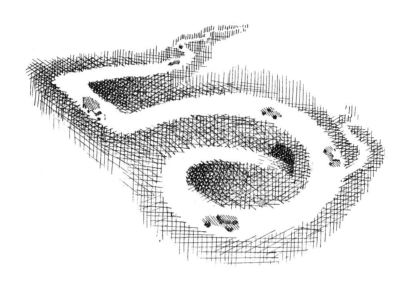

Six is a cherry with a long stem;
In summer I eat any number of them.

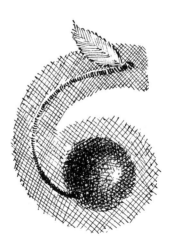

Seven is the edge of a ship out at sea;
You can't see the captain, for he's taking tea.

Eight is a number of which I am fond;
It goes skating in circles over the pond.
It's also a double top you can spin,
Or a very fat cat with its tail tucked in.

Nine is the full moon caught up in a tree:
Will somebody tall please release it for me?

THE STRAY CAT

It's just an old alley cat
that has followed us all the way home.

It hasn't a star on its forehead,
or a silky satiny coat.

No proud tiger stripes, no dainty tread,
no elegant velvet throat.

It's a splotchy, blotchy
city cat, not pretty cat,
a rough little tough little bag of old bones.

"Beauty," we shall call you.
"Beauty, come in."

NIGHT SONG

Hushaby, hushaby, hushaby,
On velvet hooves the horses
Of darkness are riding on by.
Hushaby, hushaby, hushaby,
Galloping over the velvet sky.

> *Close your eyes and within the stillness*
> *You will hear the silent tune*
> *Of the spinning of the planets*
> *And the circling round of the moon.*

Hushaby, hushaby, hushaby,
On velvet wings the swallows
Of darkness are flying on high.
Hushaby, hushaby, hushaby,
Feathering over the velvet sky.

> *Close your eyes and within the stillness*
> *You will hear the silent tune*
> *Of the spinning of the planets*
> *And the circling round of the moon.*

Hushaby, hushaby, hushaby,
On velvet waves the dolphins
Of darkness arise from the deep.
Hushaby, hushaby, hushaby,
Sleep . . . sleep . . . sleep.

Close your eyes and within the stillness
You will hear the silent tune
Of the spinning of the planets
And the circling round of the moon.

WITH *Catch A Little Rhyme* Eve Merriam completes a trilogy of poetry books for children that really begins with this book. For here she has poems that will appeal to the primary child— some that will be read to them and some they will read for themselves. These can then be followed by her two earlier books, *There Is No Rhyme for Silver* and *It Doesn't Always Have to Rhyme,* each of which develops further the concept of what poetry really is. These books have all grown out of her conviction that there should be poetry for young people that is fun and yet memorable and in a modern vein. They have been written with the same care and out of the same depth as her numerous books of adult poetry. Among these, *Family Circle,* her first book, was awarded the Yale Series of Younger Poets Prize and was published with an introduction by Archibald MacLeish.

Miss Merriam has also conducted a weekly radio series on modern poetry for radio station WQXR in New York, and written poetry for newspapers, fiction and non-fiction for magazines, and picture books for children.